Make it ea

English

Quick Tests

Age 8-9

Louis Fidge

Test 1 Verbs

The helicopter **flew** in the sky.

Helicopters **are** flying machines.

Many verbs are **doing** words.
They describe **actions**.

Some verbs are **being** words.

<u>Underline</u> the verb in each sentence.

1. A footballer <u>kicks</u> a ball.

2. Some birds <u>catch</u> worms.

3. Caterpillars <u>become</u> butterflies or moths.

4. The car <u>raced</u> along the road.

5. The girl is very <u>scruffy</u>.

6. Mr Patel was <u>late</u>.

7. The train <u>left</u> the station.

8. Aeroplanes <u>land</u> on runways.

9. The mouse <u>ran</u> into the hole.

10. The lady <u>sat</u> in her garden.

11. A baker <u>makes</u> bread.

12. I <u>invited</u> Anna to my party.

13. The worm <u>wriggled</u> away.

14. The children <u>are noisy</u>.

15. The lady <u>showed</u> us the way.

Colour in your score

Test 1

Test 2 Phonemes

A **phoneme** is the **smallest unit of sound**. A phoneme may be made up of **one or more** letters which make **one sound**.

b + oy = boy
(two phonemes)

g + ir + l = girl
(three phonemes)

Choose the correct phoneme to complete each word.

1. holid_____   (ai/ay)

2. barr_____   (oa/ow)

3. p_____ll   (u/oo)

4. tr_____   (ue/ew)

5. v_____ce   (oy/oi)

6. pr_____l   (ow/ou)

7. str_____   (aw/au)

8. s_____ce   (or/au)

9. cr_____d   (ou/ow)

10. th_____d   (er/ir)

11. sc_____   (are/ere)

12. c_____ly   (er/ur)

13. b_____   (ear/ere)

14. p_____   (ere/air)

15. th_____   (air/ere)

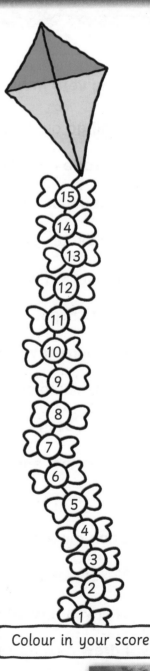

Colour in your score

15
14
13
12
11
10
9
8
7
6
5
4
3
2
1

Test 2

Test 3 Verb tenses

Verbs can be written in different **tenses**.

This happened in the **past**. The verb is in the **past tense**.

This is happening **now**. The verb is in the **present tense**.

This will happen in the **future**. The verb is in the **future tense**.

Say if the verb in bold is past, present or future tense.

1. I **will go** out to play after tea. _____

2. We **rode** our bikes. _____

3. I **am swimming** in the sea. _____

4. The girl **dropped** her bag in the mud. _____

5. Tomorrow I **will take** my ruler to school. _____

6. I **like** crisps. _____

7. My mum **gave** me some lunch. _____

8. In the summer I **will fly** on a plane. _____

9. I **sleep** in the top bunk. _____

10. My brother **snores**. _____

11. The car **crashed** into a wall. _____

12. Soon the ambulance **will arrive**. _____

13. Next week I **will leave** for Paris. _____

14. Last year I **went** to Spain. _____

15. I **drew** a picture in my book. _____

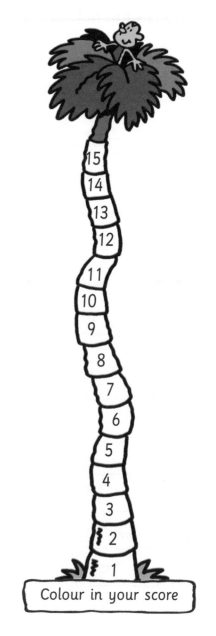

Colour in your score

Test 3

Test 4 Syllables

When we say a word slowly, we can hear how it may be broken down into **smaller parts** called **syllables**. Each syllable must contain at least **one vowel**.

car (one syllable)

ri/ding (two syllables)

car/a/van (three syllables)

Say these words slowly.

Write if they have one, two or three syllables.

1. bike   _____

2. scooter   _____

3. yesterday   _____

4. sun   _____

5. afternoon   _____

6. summer   _____

7. shoes   _____

8. dentist   _____

9. weekend   _____

10. sandwich   _____

11. rain   _____

12. boat   _____

13. syllable   _____

14. tonight   _____

15. tomorrow   _____

Colour in your score

Test 4

Test 5 Suffixes

A **suffix** is a **group of letters** we add to the **end of a word**.
A suffix changes the **meaning** of a word or the **job the word does**.

paint (verb)   painter (noun)

Add either the suffix **er** or **or** to make these verbs into nouns. Take care with the spelling.

1. bake   _____

2. visit   _____

3. detect   _____

4. clean   _____

5. build   _____

6. edit   _____

7. calculate _____

8. dance   _____

9. sail   _____

10. print   _____

11. radiate _____

12. swim   _____

13. inspect _____

14. act   _____

15. skate   _____

Colour in your score

Test 5

Test 6 Alphabetical order

Many reference books are organised in **alphabetical order**.

light   lion   lizard

These words are organised in alphabetical order according to the **third** letter.

granny   grapes   grass

These words are organised in alphabetical order according to the **fourth** letter.

Order these words according to their third letter.

1. acrobat   act   acorn   _____

2. bacon   baby   badge   _____

3. beach   between   bend   _____

4. daisy   dance   dam   _____

5. door   dock   doughnut   _____

6. fig   fire   film   _____

Order these words according to their fourth letter.

7. climb   cliff   clinic   _____

8. drink   drill   drift   _____

9. earth   early   earn   _____

10. margarine   marsh   market _____

11. herring   herb   hero   _____

12. blanket   blast   black   _____

13. brown   brother   broccoli _____

14. script   scrap   screen   _____

15. through   thrust   threw   _____

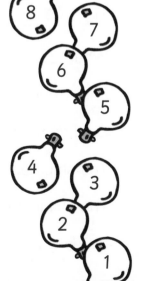

Colour in your score

Test 6

Test 7 Homophones

Homophones are words that **sound alike** but have **different spellings** and **different meanings**.

I **heard** a **herd** of elephants coming towards me.

Choose the correct word to complete each sentence.

1. The _____ shone in the sky. (sun/son)

2. I _____ my bike. (rode/road)

3. He ate the _____ cake. (hole/whole)

4. I had a _____ of pie. (peace/piece)

5. I tied a _____ in the string. (not/knot)

6. You have to _____ an apple. (peal/peel)

7. I measured my _____. (waste/waist)

8. The man took the quickest _____. (route/root)

9. The _____ landed at the airport. (plane/plain)

10. What _____ do you eat for breakfast? (cereal/serial)

11. It is wrong to _____. (steal/steel)

12. Bald men have no _____ on their heads. (hairs/hares)

13. The ship had two _____. (sales/sails)

14. The children took _____ bags. (there/their)

15. It's easy to get _____. (board/bored)

Colour in your score

Test 7

Test 8 Adverbs

Adverbs tell us **more about verbs**. Many adverbs tell us **how** something happened. Many adverbs end in **ly**.

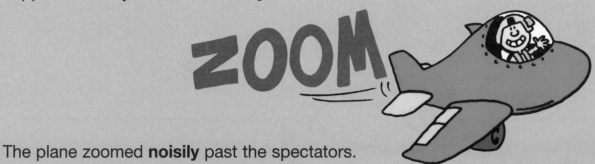

The plane zoomed **noisily** past the spectators.

<u>Underline</u> the adverb in each sentence.

1. The boy ate his lunch greedily.

2. The sun shone brightly.

3. I smiled shyly at my aunt.

4. The car moved off slowly.

5. Bravely the knight faced the dragon.

6. The old lady sat down tiredly.

7. Carefully I picked up the model made of matchsticks.

8. The man shouted angrily.

9. Do your work neatly.

10. The thief hurriedly left the shop.

11. Happily I accepted the winner's medal.

12. Are you sitting comfortably?

13. The dog growled fiercely at the stranger.

14. Suddenly it began to rain.

15. I smiled cheerfully.

Colour in your score

Test 8

Test 9 Words within words

Look for **smaller words** hidden inside **longer words** to help you to spell them.

An island **is land** surrounded by water.

sandwich	piece	believe
sword	bicycle	business
chocolate	country	government
heard	jewellery	mathematics
present	restaurant	soldier

Which word above has the following small word 'hiding' in it?

1. bus _____

2. try _____

3. over _____

4. word _____

5. old _____

6. sent _____

7. sand _____

8. ant _____

9. lie _____

10. pie _____

11. icy _____

12. ear _____

13. well _____

14. late _____

15. the _____

Colour in your score

Test 9

Test 10 **Adverbs again**

quick – quickly

We can just add **ly** to many adjectives to make adverbs.

merry – merrily

If the word ends in **y**, we change the **y** to **i** and add **ly**.

miserable – miserably

If the word ends in **le**, we often drop the **le** and add **ly**.

Change these adjectives into adverbs ending in ly.

1. sweet _____

2. hungry _____

3. simple _____

4. plain _____

5. proud _____

6. noble _____

7. idle _____

8. glad _____

9. angry _____

10. feeble _____

11. easy _____

12. willing _____

13. lazy _____

14. possible _____

15. steady _____

Colour in your score

Test 10

Test 11 Adjectives

An **adjective** is a **describing** word. It gives us more information about the **noun**.

The **clever** cat walked on the **wooden** fence to the **smelly** dustbin.

Choose the best adjective to go with each noun.

1. a _____ dragon   (fierce/sour)

2. an _____ troll   (old/ugly)

3. a _____ eel   (slippery/cold)

4. a _____ bee   (tired/busy)

5. a _____ weight   (heavy/red)

6. a _____ wind   (quiet/howling)

7. a _____ sword   (kind/sharp)

8. a _____ cave   (full/dark)

9. a _____ drink   (fizzy/damp)

10. a _____ tyre   (open/flat)

11. an _____ door   (open/attractive)

12. a _____ tree   (tall/sloping)

13. a _____ sea   (silly/rough)

14. a _____ pencil   (blunt/calm)

15. a _____ sheep   (woolly/muddy)

Colour in your score

Test 11

Test 12 **Similes**

A **simile** is when we **compare** one thing with another.

He was **as slow as a snail**.

Choose the best adjective to complete each simile.

heavy	black	red	quiet	playful	
	sweet	soft	green	smooth	wise
white	fierce	cool	light	slippery	

1. as _____ as honey

2. as _____ as a kitten

3. as _____ as silk

4. as _____ as butter

5. as _____ as a cucumber

6. as _____ as an owl

7. as _____ as beetroot

8. as _____ as a lion

9. as _____ as grass

10. as _____ as an eel

11. as _____ as snow

12. as _____ as lead

13. as _____ as a feather

14. as _____ as a mouse

15. as _____ as coal

Colour in your score

Test 12

Test 13 Common word endings

Look for **common letter patterns** to help your spelling.

catch   switch   hutch

badge	watch	light	dodge	nudge	
	might	sight	fetch	hutch	fight
hedge	bright	stitch	botch	bridge	

Find and write the dge words in alphabetical order.

1. _____   2. _____   3. _____

4. _____   5. _____

Find and write the tch words in alphabetical order.

6. _____   7. _____   8. _____

9. _____   10. _____

Find and write the **ight** words in alphabetical order.

11. _____   12. _____   13. _____

14. _____   15. _____

Colour in your score

Test 13

Test 14 Comparing adjectives

When we **compare two nouns** we use a **comparative adjective**.

When we **compare three or more** nouns we use a **superlative adjective**.

A mouse is *fast*.   A rabbit is *faster*.   A leopard is the *fastest*.

Fill in the missing adjective. Take care with the spelling.

1.	slow	_____	slowest
2.	smooth	smoother	_____
3.	soft	softer	_____
4.	light	_____	lightest
5.	safe	_____	safest
6.	wide	wider	_____
7.	large	larger	_____
8.	wet	_____	wettest
9.	big	bigger	_____
10.	hot	_____	hottest
11.	lucky	_____	luckiest
12.	noisy	noisier	_____
13.	busy	_____	busiest
14.	pretty	_____	prettiest
15.	muddy	muddier	_____

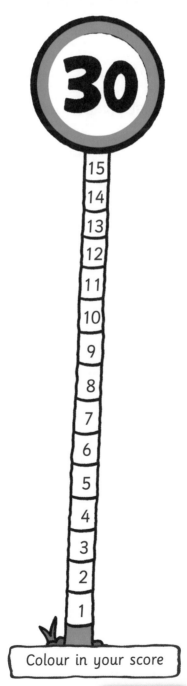

Colour in your score

Test 15 More suffixes

A **suffix** is a **group of letters** we add to the **end** of a word.

A suffix changes the **meaning** of the word or the **job the word does**.

magic – magic**al**

Choose the correct suffix to complete each word.

1. music_____ (al/ous)

2. fashion_____ (able/ible)

3. educat_____ (ment/ion)

4. comic_____ (ment/al)

5. amuse_____ (ous/ment)

6. invis_____ (able/ible)

7. employ_____ (ment/al)

8. inspect_____ (ion/ment)

9. person_____ (tion/al)

10. arrange_____ (ion/ment)

11. comfort_____ (able/ible)

12. entertain_____ (ment/al)

13. sens_____ (able/ible)

14. season_____ (al/ise)

15. act_____ (ment/ion)

Colour in your score

15
14
13
12
11
10
9
8
7
6
5
4
3
2
1

Test 16 Gender words

Nouns may be classified according to their **gender**.

a woman

a man

Nouns which refer to
females are **feminine**.

Nouns which refer to
males are **masculine**.

Use these nouns to complete the chart below.

princess   grandfather   mother   man   bridegroom
daughter   husband   countess   girl   uncle   king
sister   nephew   headmistress   duke

	masculine	feminine
1.	father	_____
2.	_____	wife
3.	boy	_____
4.	prince	_____
5.	_____	aunt
6.	_____	woman
7.	_____	queen
8.	_____	bride
9.	brother	_____
10.	_____	grandmother
11.	headmaster	_____
12.	_____	niece
13.	count	_____
14.	_____	duchess
15.	son	_____

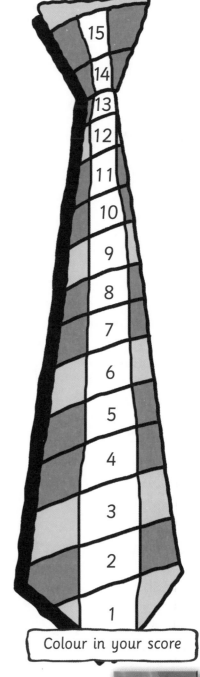

15
14
13
12
11
10
9
8
7
6
5
4
3
2
1

Colour in your score

Test 16

Test 17 **Contractions**

We sometimes **shorten** a word by **leaving out** some letters.
These shortened words are called **contractions**.
We use an **apostrophe** to show where letters have been left out.

I'm going on holiday.

I'm = I am

Match up each contraction with its longer form.

1.	can't	we have
2.	didn't	do not
3.	we've	can not
4.	you'll	it is
5.	that's	did not
6.	don't	I would
7.	doesn't	shall not
8.	you're	does not
9.	shouldn't	they are
10.	we'll	you will
11.	I'd	will not
12.	it's	should not
13.	they're	we will
14.	shan't	that is
15.	won't	you are

Colour in your score

Test 17

Test 18 Commas

Long ago, dinosaurs
roamed the earth.

Commas are used to separate **extra bits** that are **added** to sentences.

The car, a red one, was
parked outside the shop.

Commas help to **break up** longer sentences **into smaller parts**.

Put the missing commas in each of these sentences.

1. That boy the smaller one shouted rude names at me.

2. Don't do that Sam!

3. Pass me my cup of tea please.

4. Feeling rather tired Goldilocks sat down on the chair.

5. Let's go out shall we?

6. Whenever I can I like to go out.

7. Pick up your bag Anna.

8. The dog a spotted Dalmatian escaped from the garden.

9. If I can find one I always buy a comic.

10. Quiet please!

11. No I don't want a sandwich.

12. Whether it's rugby or football I enjoy the game.

13. What's the matter Mrs Shah?

14. Once upon a time there lived an ugly troll.

15. That's very nice thank you.

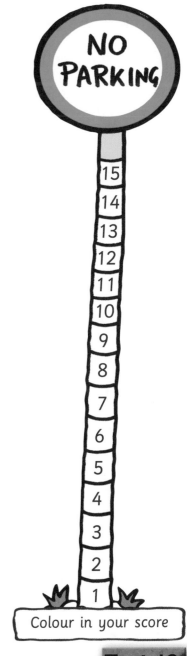

NO PARKING

15
14
13
12
11
10
9
8
7
6
5
4
3
2
1

Colour in your score

Test 18

Test 19 Word order

Sometimes when we **change the order** of words, it **changes the meaning** of the sentence.

The dog chased the postman.   The postman chased the dog.

Rearrange the words in these sentences so they make sense.

1. The sandwich ate a man.   _____

2. The car got into the prince.   _____

3. The crown put on his king.   _____

4. The laugh made us clown.   _____

5. The tree climbed the squirrel. _____

6. The piano played the teacher. _____

7. The trunk lifted its elephant. _____

8. The ball kicked a footballer. _____

9. Some boots wore children.   _____

10. The runway landed on the plane. _____

11. An egg fried the girl.   _____

12. The bone picked up the dog.   _____

13. The television is watching Sam. _____

14. A tunnel went through the train. _____

15. Stripes have tigers.   _____

Colour in your score

Test 20 Apostrophes marking possession

We use an **apostrophe** to show **ownership** (that something belongs to someone).

When there is **only one** owner, we usually write **'s**.

When there is **more than one** owner, we usually write **s'**.

the boy's books
(the books belong to one boy)

the boys' books
(the books belong to more than one boy)

Write the shortened form of each phrase.

1. the bike belongs to the girl _____the girl's bike_____

2. the pen belongs to the boy _____

3. the car belongs to the man _____

4. the cup belongs to my brother _____

5. the nuts belong to the squirrels _____

6. the ship belongs to the sailors _____

7. the school belongs to the teachers _____

8. the tie belongs to Sam _____

9. the bag belongs to Dr Smith _____

10. the cubs belong to the lion _____

11. the bananas belong to the monkeys _____

12. the ball belongs to the footballers _____

13. the guitar belongs to the singer _____

14. the barn belongs to the farmer _____

15. the hose belongs to the fire-fighters _____

15
14
13
12
11
10
9
8
7
6
5
4
3
2
1

Colour in your score

Test 20

Test 21 Compound words

A **compound word** is made up of **two smaller words** joined together.

cup + board = cupboard

Write these compound words as two separate words.

1. passport   _____ _____

2. birthday   _____ _____

3. overseas   _____ _____

4. broadcast   _____ _____

5. driftwood   _____ _____

6. rainforest   _____ _____

7. courtyard   _____ _____

8. trapdoor   _____ _____

9. horseback   _____ _____

10. underground _____ _____

11. stairway   _____ _____

12. cloakroom   _____ _____

13. roundabout   _____ _____

14. keyhole   _____ _____

15. breakfast   _____ _____

Colour in your score

Test 21

Test 22 Diminutives

Diminutives are words that imply something **small**.

duck – duckling

frog – tadpole

A **diminutive** can sometimes be made by adding a **suffix**.

A **diminutive** can sometimes be a **different word altogether**.

Match up each noun with its correct diminutive.

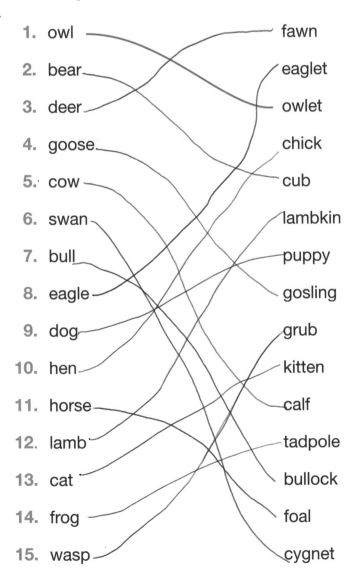

1. owl
2. bear
3. deer
4. goose
5. cow
6. swan
7. bull
8. eagle
9. dog
10. hen
11. horse
12. lamb
13. cat
14. frog
15. wasp

fawn
eaglet
owlet
chick
cub
lambkin
puppy
gosling
grub
kitten
calf
tadpole
bullock
foal
cygnet

Colour in your score

Test 22

Test 23 **Surprising sounds**

Letters do not always sound the way we expect them to.

wa**sh**

When **a** comes after **w** it often sounds like **o**.

swar**m**

When **ar** comes after **w** it often sounds like **or**.

wor**m**

When **or** comes after **w** it often sounds like **er**.

Choose a, ar or or to complete each word.

1. w_____sh

2. wh_____f

3. w_____ld

4. w_____th

5. sw_____m

6. w_____ddle

7. w_____nder

8. dw_____f

9. w_____tch

10. w_____se

11. w_____rrant

12. w_____p

13. w_____k

14. w_____thy

15. w_____llet

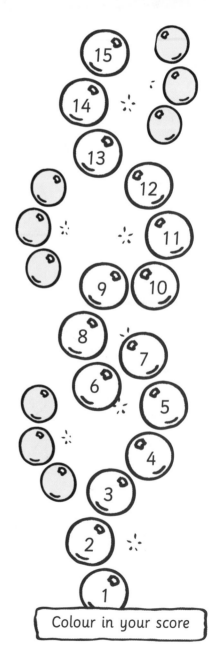

Colour in your score

Test 23

Test 24 Types of sentences

There are **four** different **types of sentences**.

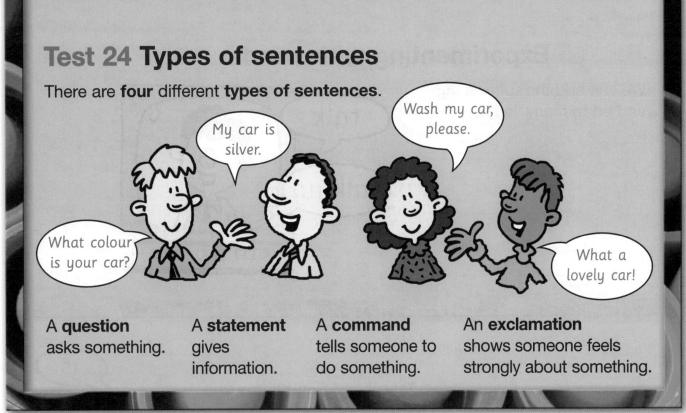

A **question**
asks something.

A **statement**
gives
information.

A **command**
tells someone to
do something.

An **exclamation**
shows someone feels
strongly about something.

Write what type of sentence each of these is.

1. The door is shut.   _____

2. Where is my bag?   _____

3. Go and have a bath.   _____

4. What a muddy T-shirt!   _____

5. When are you going?   _____

6. It's not fair!   _____

7. I'm going to bed.   _____

8. Turn off the television.   _____

9. I think that's wonderful!   _____

10. How did you get lost?   _____

11. Tom likes tennis.   _____

12. Cut the paper with scissors.   _____

13. Put the kettle on.   _____

14. Help!   _____

15. Who are you going with?   _____

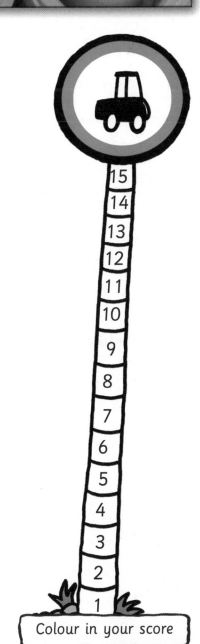

15
14
13
12
11
10
9
8
7
6
5
4
3
2
1

Colour in your score

Test 24

Test 25 **Experimenting with words**

We can add the suffixes **ing** and **ed** to many verbs.

talk – talk**ing** – talk**ed**

Add the suffix ing to these verbs. Take care! Sometimes you may have to change the spelling of the root verb.

1. look   _____

2. tap   _____

3. make   _____

4. shrug   _____

5. hop   _____

6. shout   _____

7. use   _____

8. carry   _____

Add the suffix ed to these verbs. Take care! Sometimes you may have to change the spelling of the root verb.

9. pin   _____

10. try   _____

11. marry   _____

12. slip   _____

13. fade   _____

14. hope   _____

15. walk   _____

CHATTER CHATTER CHATTER CHATTER CHATTER

15 14 13 12 11 10 9 8 7 6 5 4 3 2 1

Colour in your score

Test 25

Test 26 The word endings tion and sion

The two common word endings **tion** and **sion** sometimes get confused.

invita**tion**

The **tion** at the end of words sounds like **shun**.

televi**sion**

The **sion** at the end of words sounds like **zhon**.

The ending of each of these words is wrong.
Write each word correctly.

1. conversasion _____

2. explotion _____

3. sucsion _____

4. invation _____

5. confution _____

6. preparasion _____

7. creasion _____

8. revition _____

9. competision _____

10. populasion _____

11. divition _____

12. composision _____

13. conclution _____

14. inclution _____

15. fracsion _____

Colour in your score

Test 26

Test 27 **The word endings able and ible**

The two common word endings **able** and **ible** sometimes get confused.

comfort + able = comfortable

It is often possible to see the root word when **able** is added.

horror + ible = horrible

It is not always possible to see the root word when **ible** is added.

Choose able or ible to complete each word.

1. poss_____

2. reason_____

3. terr_____

4. reli_____

5. fashion_____

6. flex_____

7. remark_____

8. suit_____

9. respons_____

10. revers_____

11. sens_____

12. valu_____

13. miser_____

14. favour_____

15. vis_____

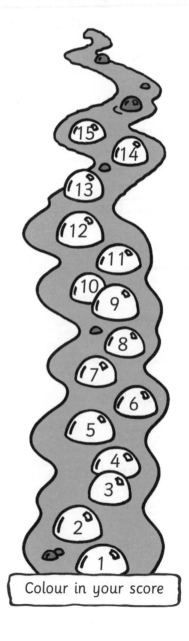

Colour in your score

Test 27

Test 28 Common letter strings

Some **letter strings** are very **common** – but they do not always make the same sound.

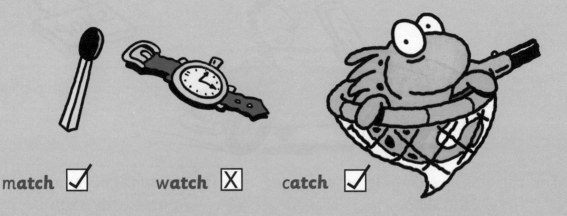

match ✓   watch ☒   catch ✓

<u>Underline</u> the odd word out in each set.

1. tough   cough   rough

2. five   hive   give

3. have   wave   gave

4. lost   cost   post

5. how   glow   now

6. love   glove   move

7. height   eight   weight

8. though   dough   trough

9. bear   near   fear

10. good   hood   blood

11. vase   case   base

12. cough   trough   through

13. stone   gone   bone

14. caught   daughter   laugh

15. wallet   mallet   pallet

Colour in your score

Test 28

Test 29 Conjunctions

A **conjunction** is a **joining** word. It may be used to join two sentences.

The car was speeding. It passed
the shop.

(two sentences)

The car was speeding **as** It
passed the shop.

(one sentence with a conjunction)

Find and <u>underline</u> the conjunction in each sentence.

1. It rained heavily but we carried on with the game.

2. The teacher opened the door and the children came in.

3. I went to the shop but it was closed.

4. The children went outside and played in the garden.

5. The monkey will not come unless you give it a banana.

6. He was given the prize because he deserved it.

7. I got lost when I drove through the town.

8. I gave her another sweet as she had eaten the last one.

9. He bought me the present although he couldn't afford it.

10. Do not climb the tree or you might fall.

11. You will not pass the test if you don't try harder.

12. I went indoors when it began raining.

13. The girl will not go to school unless her mother brings her.

14. We started early so we would finish in time for tea.

15. I was nervous as I hadn't seen my uncle for a long time.

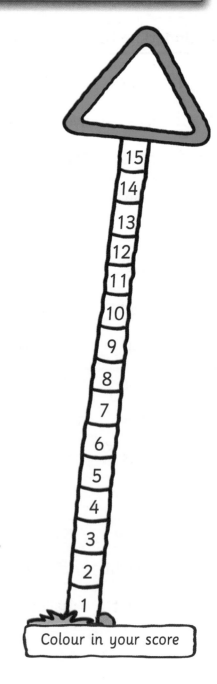

Colour in your score

15
14
13
12
11
10
9
8
7
6
5
4
3
2
1

Test 30 Positive and negative

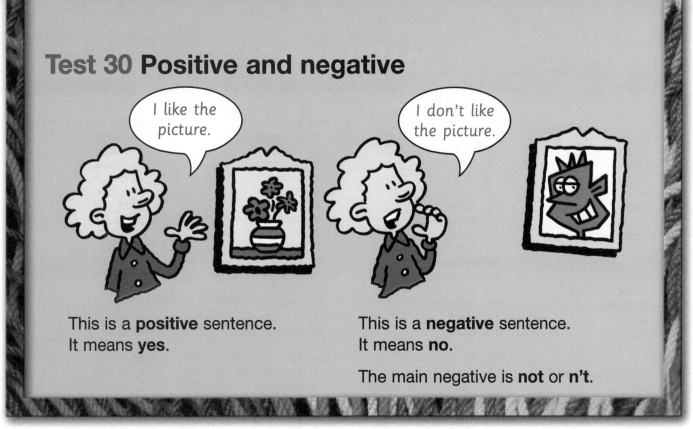

I like the picture.

This is a **positive** sentence.
It means **yes**.

I don't like the picture.

This is a **negative** sentence.
It means **no**.

The main negative is **not** or **n't**.

Say whether each sentence is positive or negative.

1. I like sweets. _____

2. Lee was not a good boy. _____

3. It did not stop raining. _____

4. Ben won the race. _____

5. I didn't do my homework last night. _____

6. You should always smile. _____

7. You should never tell lies. _____

8. My drawing is nice. _____

9. I don't like spelling. _____

10. I hate maths. _____

11. Don't shout. _____

12. You must not run. _____

13. The old lady could not lift the box. _____

14. I can't whistle. _____

15. I can knit. _____

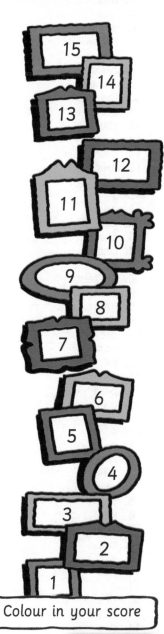

Colour in your score

ANSWERS

Test 1
1. kicks
2. catch
3. become
4. raced
5. is
6. was
7. left
8. land
9. ran
10. sat
11. makes
12. invited
13. wriggled
14. are
15. showed

Test 2
The correct phoneme is in **bold**.
1. holid**ay**
2. narr**ow**
3. p**u**ll
4. tr**ue**
5. v**oi**ce
6. pr**ow**l
7. stra**w**
8. s**au**ce
9. cr**ow**d
10. th**ir**d
11. sc**are**
12. c**ur**ly
13. b**ear**
14. p**air**
15. th**ere**

Test 3
1. future
2. past
3. present
4. past
5. future
6. present
7. past
8. future
9. present
10. present
11. past
12. future
13. future
14. past
15. past

Test 4
1. one
2. two
3. three
4. one
5. three
6. two
7. one
8. two
9. two
10. two
11. one
12. one
13. three
14. two
15. three

Test 5
1. baker
2. visitor
3. detector
4. cleaner
5. builder
6. editor
7. calculator
8. dancer
9. sailor
10. printer
11. radiator
12. swimmer
13. inspector
14. actor
15. skater

Test 6
1. acorn acrobat act
2. baby bacon badge
3. beach bend between
4. daisy dam dance
5. dock door doughnut
6. fig film fire
7. cliff climb clinic
8. drift drill drink
9. early earn earth
10. margarine market marsh
11. herb hero herring
12. black blanket blast
13. broccoli brother brown
14. scrap screen script
15. threw through thrust

Test 7
1. sun
2. rode
3. whole
4. piece
5. knot
6. peel
7. waist
8. route
9. plane
10. cereal
11. steal
12. hairs
13. sails
14. their
15. bored

Test 8
1. greedily
2. brightly
3. shyly
4. slowly
5. Bravely
6. tiredly
7. Carefully
8. angrily
9. neatly
10. hurriedly
11. Happily
12. comfortably
13. fiercely
14. Suddenly
15. cheerfully

Test 9
1. business
2. country
3. government
4. sword
5. soldier
6. present
7. sandwich
8. restaurant
9. believe
10. piece
11. bicycle
12. heard
13. jewellery
14. chocolate
15. mathematics

Test 10
1. sweetly
2. hungrily
3. simply
4. plainly
5. proudly
6. nobly
7. idly
8. gladly
9. angrily
10. feebly
11. easily
12. willingly
13. lazily
14. possibly
15. steadily

Test 11
1. fierce
2. ugly
3. slippery
4. busy
5. heavy
6. howling
7. sharp
8. dark
9. fizzy
10. flat
11. open
12. tall
13. rough
14. blunt
15. woolly

Test 12
1. sweet
2. playful
3. smooth
4. soft
5. cool
6. wise
7. red
8. fierce
9. green
10. slippery
11. white
12. heavy
13. light
14. quiet
15. black

Test 13
1. badge
2. bridge
3. dodge
4. hedge
5. nudge
6. botch
7. fetch
8. hutch
9. stitch
10. watch
11. bright
12. fight
13. light
14. might
15. sight

Test 14
1. slower
2. smoothest
3. softest
4. lighter
5. safer
6. widest
7. largest
8. wetter
9. biggest
10. hotter
11. luckier
12. noisiest
13. busier
14. prettier
15. muddiest

Test 15
The correct suffix is in **bold**.
1. music**al**
2. fashion**able**
3. educat**ion**
4. comic**al**
5. amuse**ment**
6. invis**ible**
7. employ**ment**
8. inspec**tion**
9. person**al**
10. arrange**ment**
11. comfort**able**
12. entertain**ment**
13. sens**ible**
14. season**al**
15. act**ion**

Test 16
1. mother
2. husband
3. girl
4. princess
5. uncle
6. man
7. king
8. bridegroom
9. sister
10. grandfather
11. headmistress
12. nephew
13. countess
14. duke
15. daughter